EXPECT

Written and illustrated by

dolli tingle

·Stardust·
·.Books·
The C. R. Gibson Company
Norwalk, Connecticut

You've packed all our bags
With things you won't use!
You're having a baby!
Not taking a cruise!

IMPORTANT INFO

Doctor's name_____

Doctor's phone no._____

Hospital_____

Hospital address_____

Hospital phone no._____

when Baby is expected

Date_____

TO TAKE TO HOSPITAL

Tooth brush	Cosmetics	Robe
Tooth paste	Shower cap	Tissues
Hand mirror	Night gowns	Pen
Face cloth	Bed jacket	Paper
Comb, brush	Slippers	This book

Going home clothes for baby and me.

When you wanted pickles
And Chili Con Carne
I should have been given
Fair warning.
But where will I buy
A fresh Strawberry Pie
When it's now two o'clock
In the morning?

WHAT DOC SAYS I SHOULD EAT

_____

_____

_____

_____

_____

_____

_____

_____

_____

_____

WHAT I CRAVE !

_____

_____

_____

_____

_____

I'LL KEEP MY WEIGHT DOWN

My normal weight is

.... lbs.

Date	Weight
_____	_____
_____	_____
_____	_____
_____	_____
_____	_____
_____	_____
_____	_____
_____	_____
_____	_____
_____	_____
_____	_____
_____	_____
_____	_____
_____	_____
_____	_____
_____	_____

My dear!
You're looking marvelous!
You've such a lovely glow!
A baby coming?
Who'd have guessed!
On you it doesn't show!

BOY'S NAMES
WE LIKE BEST

_____

_____

_____

_____

_____

_____

THE ONE WE CHOSE

_____

WHY : _____

_____

I'd like to name him John
Or Andrew.
But George is good
Or Dave or Earl.
Let's call him Tom
Or maybe Robert.
Unless, of course,
He is a girl!

If we name her for your Mother
Then MY folks will have a fit.
If we name her for MY Mother,
Then YOUR Mom might fret a bit.
I once knew a girl called Angel.
But I see THAT wouldn't do.
So, I think the safest thing is
Just to name her after you!

GIRL'S NAMES
WE LIKE BEST

_____

_____

_____

_____

_____

_____

_____

THE ONE WE CHOSE

_____

WHY: _____

_____

LAYETTE

- ☐ Diapers { 3 to 4 dozen if washed at home / 90-100 per week if from service
- ☐ Diaper pins and pail
- ☐ Cotton shirts (4-6)
- ☐ Gowns, wrappers (4-6)
- ☐ Dress and slip (2)
- ☐ Booties (2-3 pair)
- ☐ Sacques, sweaters (2)
- ☐ Waterproof pants (2-4)
- ☐ Receiving blankets (6)
- ☐ Rompers
- ☐ Knit creepers
- ☐ Sun suits
- ☐ Bunting or
- ☐ Coat and bonnet
- ☐ Diaper bag
- ☐ Carriage and robe
- ☐ Baby record book

- ☐ Bassinet or crib with crib bumpers
- ☐ Waterproof sheets (2 large, 1 small)
- ☐ Waterproof mattress
- ☐ Quilted pads (4)
- ☐ Crib blankets (4)
- ☐ Reclining infant seat
- ☐ Car bed
- ☐ Crib sheets (3-4)
- ☐ Playpen and pad
- ☐ Chest of drawers
- ☐ Toilet seat
- ☐ Car seat

- ☐ Bathinette or tub with table top
- ☐ Bath towels (3-4)
- ☐ Toiletries tray
- ☐ Brush and comb
- ☐ Baby oil, lotion, powder
- ☐ Sterile cotton balls, swabs
- ☐ Washcloths (3-4)
- ☐ Baby soap
- ☐ Baby shampoo
- ☐ Baby scale
- ☐ Thermometers

- ☐ High chair
- ☐ Feeding dish, spoon
- ☐ Bottle, nipple brush
- ☐ Bibs
- ☐ Bottle warmer
- ☐ Sterilizer
- ☐ Nursers { 8 ounce (8 to 10) / 4 ounce (2-4 for water or juice)

Don't tell me that our baby
Will be wearing all this stuff.
If we should have quadruplets
It is still more than enough!
You've knitted fourteen sweaters
And made booties by the score.
Instead of one small baby
What we should have is a store!

Just simple housework exercise
I heard the Doctor say.
So, why this sudden urge to do
Spring cleaning every day?

KEEPING IN TRIM

If Doc okays exercises

I'll go for walks

I'll sit like a tailor

I'll lie on the floor, hold my breath, stretch arms and legs. Then open mouth, slowly exhale and relax.

I'll lie on floor, feet together, knees up, arms out. I'll roll hips to right 'til knees touch floor. Then roll left in same way. I'll repeat slowly several times.

The cake is delicious!
The table's so cute!
And not only that, dear,
Just think of the loot!

SHOWERS
AND PARTIES

How sweet of you to bring a gift
And drop in for a visit.
I'm sure it's just what baby needs.
Now, tell me, dear, what is it?

GIFTS

Check when acknowledged

- ☐ —————————————————
- ☐ —————————————————
- ☐ —————————————————
- ☐ —————————————————

————————————— ☐
————————————— ☐
————————————— ☐
————————————— ☐

- ☐ —————————————————
- ☐ —————————————————
- ☐ —————————————————
- ☐ —————————————————

————————————— ☐
————————————— ☐
————————————— ☐
————————————— ☐

GIFTS

- ☐ ———————————————————
- ☐ ———————————————————
- ☐ ———————————————————
- ☐ ———————————————————

——————————————————— ☐
——————————————————— ☐
——————————————————— ☐
——————————————————— ☐

- ☐ ———————————————————
- ☐ ———————————————————
- ☐ ———————————————————
- ☐ ———————————————————

——————————————————— ☐
——————————————————— ☐
——————————————————— ☐
——————————————————— ☐

 # GIFTS

- [ ] ———————————————————
- [ ] ———————————————————
- [ ] ———————————————————
- [ ] ———————————————————

——————————————————— [ ]
——————————————————— [ ]
——————————————————— [ ]
——————————————————— [ ]

- [ ] ———————————————————
- [ ] ———————————————————
- [ ] ———————————————————
- [ ] ———————————————————

——————————————————— [ ]
——————————————————— [ ]
——————————————————— [ ]
——————————————————— [ ]

Is it time? Well, then get ready!
We'll be there in nothing flat!
Just stay calm, cool and collected.
Now, where DID I put my hat?

NOTES

On what happened

Don't worry about a thing,
My Love,
I've figured out the odds.
It seems there's very little chance
That we'll be having quads!

Congratulations, Sir!
It's a ....
Sir?
Sir!

Our Baby

_____

Born at_____o'clock

Date_____

Weight_____

Length_____